Affairs of the Heart

A Wedding Record

A Wedding Record

for

....

....

Contents

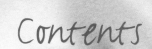

Contents

The Engagement

Bride's Page

Name

....

Date of Birth

....

Place of Birth

....

Mother

....

Father

....

Brothers/Sisters

....

....

....

....

Groom's Page

Name

....

Date of Birth

....

Place of Birth

....

Mother

....

Father

....

Brothers/Sisters

....

....

....

....

Appix Your Photograph Here

The Courtship

Where We First Met

....
....
....

When

....
....

Introduced by

....
....

First Impressions: Hers

....
....
....
....
....

First Impressions: His

....
....

Our First Date

....
....

Special Moments

....
....
....
....

AFFIX YOUR PHOTOGRAPH HERE

The Proposal

The Place

....

....

Date

....

How the Proposal Was Made

....

....

His Thoughts

....

....

....

....

Her Thoughts

....

....

....

....

The Words

....

....

How We Celebrated

....

....

....

THE ENGAGEMENT RING IS AN INCOMPLETE CIRCLE, BROKEN BY A
PRECIOUS STONE, TO SIGNIFY THE BETROTHAL. THE MARRIAGE IS
REPRESENTED BY THE COMPLETE CIRCLE OF THE WEDDING RING.

THE ENGAGEMENT RING

Choosing the Ring

....

....

The Design

....

....

Made by

....

....

History

....

....

....

....

Affix Your Photograph Here

The Announcement and Celebration

Date

Who We Told First

....

Affix Clipping

....

Their Reaction

....

....

....

....

....

....

How We Celebrated

....

....

....

....

....

Parties and Showers — Hers

Occasion

....

....

....

Hosted by

....

....

....

Guests

....

....

....

....

....

....

Gifts

....

....

....

....

....

....

PARTIES — HIS

Occasion

Hosted by

....

....

....

....

....

....

Guests

Gifts

....

....

....

....

....

....

....

....

....

....

....

....

....

....

PHOTOGRAPHS

PHOTOGRAPHS

WEDDING PLANS

Garters are worn for good luck. Often they are family heirlooms. Sometimes a blue ribbon is attached to tie in with the provberb "something old, something new, something borrowed, something blue".

TRADITIONS

Style of Wedding

....

....

....

....

....

Special Customs

....

....

....

....

....

....

....

APPIX YOUR INVITATION HERE

INVITATIONS

DESIGNED BY

....

....

NUMBER OF INVITATIONS SENT

....

WHEN SENT

....

NUMBER OF REPLIES

....

UNABLE TO ATTEND

....

....

....

....

....

Affix Your Photograph Here

Venue

Before the Ceremony

....

Special Features

....

....

Ceremony

....

Special Features

....

....

The Reception

....

Special Features

....

....

....

Affix Your Photograph Here

The Rehearsal

Date

....

Attendees

....

....

....

....

....

Special Moments

....

....

....

Dinner Venue

....

....

The Wedding Party

Affix Your Photograph Here

The Bride's Party

Attendant and Role

....

Attendant and Role

....

Attendant and Role

....

Attendant and Role

....

Attendant and Role

....

Attendant and Role

....

Attendant and Role

....

Attendant and Role

....

Attendant and Role

....

Attendant and Role

....

APPIX YOUR PHOTOGRAPH HERE

The Groom's Party

Attendant and Role   Attendant and Role

....

Attendant and Role   Attendant and Role

....

Attendant and Role   Attendant and Role

....

Attendant and Role   Attendant and Role

....

Attendant and Role   Attendant and Role

....

STYLE

Affix Your Photograph Here

The Bride's Gown

The Style of Gown

....

....

....

Fabric

....

....

Designed by

....

Made by

....

Accessories

....

....

Jewelry, Heirlooms

....

....

APPIX YOUR PHOTOGRAPH HERE

The Bride's Attendants

The style of gowns

....
....
....

Fabric

....
....

Designed by

....

Made by

....

Accessories

....
....

Jewelry, Bride's Gifts

....
....

Affix Your Photograph Here

Beauty Plan

Make-up

....

....

....

Make-up Artist

....

Hair Style

....

....

Hairdresser

....

Special Touches

....

....

....

APPIX YOUR PHOTOGRAPH HERE

The Groom

Style of Attire

....

....

....

Accessories

....

....

The Groom's Attendants

Style of Attire

....

....

....

Accessories

....

....

PHOTOGRAPHS

PHOTOGRAPHS

Finishing Touches

Affix Your Photograph Here

Bridal Flowers

Florist

....

Style

....

....

Bridal Bouquet

....

....

Attendants' Bouquets

....

....

....

Groom's Buttonhole

....

Attendants' Buttonholes

....

....

....

Special Flowers

....

....

....

APPIX YOUR PHOTOGRAPH HERE

Floral Decorations

Ceremony Arrangements

....

....

....

....

Designed by

....

....

Reception Arrangements

....

....

....

....

Designed by

....

....

PRESSED FLOWERS

MEANING OF FLOWERS

FLOWERS AND HERBS HAVE BEEN CARRIED BY BRIDES SINCE ANCIENT ROMAN TIMES.
THEY CAN BE CHOSEN FOR THEIR SPECIAL MEANINGS:

CORNFLOWER — HOPE

HONEYSUCKLE — FIDELITY

MYRTLE — CONSTANCY

ORANGE BLOSSOM — FERTILITY

RED ROSE — LOVE

VIOLET — FAITHFULNESS

WHITE CHRYSANTHEMUM — TRUTH

WHITE LILY — PURITY

MINT — VIRTUE

PARSLEY — FESTIVITY

ROSEMARY — REMEMBRANCE

SAGE — RICHES

Appix Your Photograph Here

Transport

Type

....

....

Decorations

....

....

Bride Accompanied by

....

....

....

Driven by

....

The Route

....

....

....

Affix Your Photograph Here

The Photography

Photographer

....

Special Photographs
Before the Ceremony

....

....

The Ceremony

....

....

After the Ceremony

....

....

Videographer

....

The Ceremony

Order of Service

The Ceremony

The Officiant

....

Ushers

....

....

....

Readings

....

....

....

Special Moments

....

....

....

Affix Your Photograph Here

Music

The Bridal March

Songs

....

....

....

Why they were Chosen

....

....

....

Soloists

....

....

The Departure

....

....

WEDDING RINGS ARE USUALLY WORN ON THE THIRD FINGER OF THE
LEFT HAND BECAUSE IT WAS THOUGHT THAT THIS FINGER CONTAINED
THE VEIN OF LOVE — A VEIN THAT LED DIRECTLY TO THE HEART.

The Vows

Vows Chosen

....

....

....

....

Exchange of Rings

....

....

....

History of the Rings

....

....

Special Moments

....

....

....

PHOTOGRAPHS

PHOTOGRAPHS

The Reception

Menu

Place Settings

How the Tables were Set

....

....

....

Special Details

....

....

....

Champagne

....

Wine List

....

....

....

Affix Your Photograph Here

Toasts and Speeches

Master of Ceremonies

Toasts

Speeches

Special Messages

THE ORIGIN OF THE WEDDING CAKE DATES BACK TO ANCIENT
ROME, WHEN A SPECIAL CAKE WAS BROKEN ON THE BRIDE'S
HEAD TO BRING FRUITFULNESS, AND THE GUESTS SCRAMBLED
FOR PIECES TO BRING THEM GOOD LUCK.

The Cake

Style of Cake

....

....

Made by

....

Decorated by

....

Pieces Sent

....

....

....

....

....

....

Affix Your Photograph Here

Entertainment

The Band

....

....

Soloist

....

Special Requests

....

....

....

....

....

The First Dance

....

....

Special Customs

....

....

Honeymoon

Affix Your Photograph Here

Trousseau

Travel Attire

....

....

Evening Clothes

....

....

....

Daywear

....

....

....

Lingerie

....

....

Affix Your Photograph Here

First Night and Departure

First Night Location

....

....

Supper

....

....

Champagne

....

Breakfast

....

....

Departure Luncheon

....

....

Special Memories
of the Day Before

....

....

....

....

....

....

....

Time of Departure

....

....

Affix Your Photograph Here

The Honeymoon

The Destination

....

....

The Journey

....

....

Special Times

....

....

....

....

Mementos

....

....

....

....

....

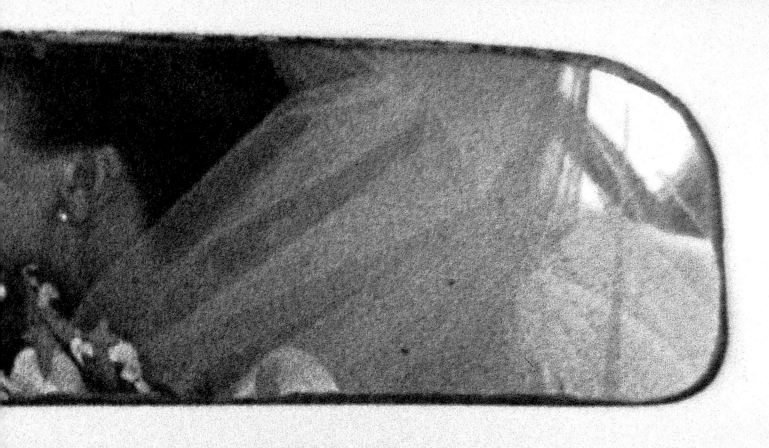

Guests
& Gifts

Guests

GUEST   REMARKS

....

....

....

....

....

....

....

....

....

....

GUESTS

GUEST   REMARKS

....

....

....

....

....

....

....

....

GUESTS

GUEST   REMARKS

....

....

....

....

....

....

....

....

....

GUESTS

GUEST   REMARKS

GUESTS

GUEST   REMARKS

....

....

....

....

....

....

....

....

....

GUESTS

GUEST   REMARKS

Guests

Guest	Remarks
....	....
....	....
....	....
....	....
....	....
....	....
....	....
....	....

GUESTS

GUEST   REMARKS

....

....

....

....

....

....

....

....

....

GUESTS

GUEST	REMARKS
....	....
....	....
....	....
....	....
....	....
....	....
....	....
....	....
....	....
....	....

GUESTS

GUEST   REMARKS

GUESTS

GUEST   REMARKS

....

....

....

....

....

....

....

....

....

....

GUESTS

GUEST

REMARKS

....

....

....

....

....

....

....

....

....

....

Gifts

Gifts	Given by
....	....
....	....
....	....
....	....
....	....
....	....
....	....
....	....
....	....

Gifts

Gifts	Given by

GIFTS

GIFTS   GIVEN BY

....

....

....

....

....

....

....

....

....

....

Gifts

Gifts   Given by

GIFTS

GIFTS   GIVEN BY

....

....

....

....

....

....

....

....

....

Gifts

Gifts	Given by
....	....
....	....
....	....
....	....
....	....
....	....
....	....
....	....
....	....

Gifts

Gifts	Given by
....	....
....	....
....	....
....	....
....	....
....	....
....	....
....	....
....	....

GIFTS

GIFTS   GIVEN BY

....

....

....

....

....

....

....

....

....

International photographer Terry Winn is recognized for his unique and innovative images. A New Zealander, his home and studio are in a historic Masonic Lodge building in Auckland.

Among many prestigious awards, he has won the Trans Tasman Champion Print Award, the New Zealand Wedding Photograph of the Year (five times) and the Photokina International Portrait Award. Terry Winn is a Fellow, with three bars, of the New Zealand Institute of Professional Photography.